DR. DOODLE'S CHRISTIANITY COMICS

Volume One, Issue Three

ON THE TRINITY

Fred Sanders

ivp

InterVarsity Press
Downers Grove, Illinois

InterVarsity Press® is the book-publishing division of InterVarsity Christian
Fellowship/USA®, a student movement active on campus at hundreds of
universities, colleges and schools of nursing in the United States of America, and a
member movement of the International Fellowship of Evangelical Students. For
information about local and regional activities, write Public Relations Dept.,
InterVarsity Christian Fellowship/USA, 6400 Schroeder Rd., P.O. Box 7895,
Madison, WI 53707-7895.

ISBN 0-8308-2243-7

Printed in the United States of America ♾

15 14 13 12 11 10 9 8 7 6 5 4 3 2 1
10 09 08 07 06 05 04 03 02 01 00 99

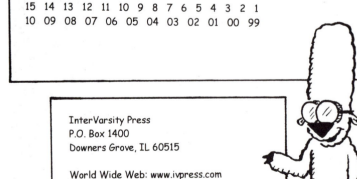

InterVarsity Press
P.O. Box 1400
Downers Grove, IL 60515

World Wide Web: www.ivpress.com

E-mail: mail@ivpress.com

CONTENTS

INTRODUCTION

ANOTHER BUSY DAY AT DR. DOCTRINE'S THEOLOGY CLINIC...

...JUST LAY OFF OF ALL THOSE *END-TIME PROPHECIES* FOR A WEEK OR TWO, AND YOU'LL BE WALKING NORMALLY AGAIN IN NO TIME.

GEE, *THANKS*, DOC!

NEXT!

THAT'D BE ME!

HEY, DOC, I WANTED TO TALK TO YOU ABOUT GETTIN' A *TRINITECTOMY!*

--A WHAT?

A *TRINITECTOMY!* YOU KNOW, WHERE YOU CUT OUT MY *TRINITY*. I FIGURED SINCE IT AIN'T *DOING* NOTHING ANYHOW, I MIGHT AS WELL HAVE IT *REMOVED*.

REMOVED!?!

WHY, THAT'S THE MOST *PREPOSTEROUS* THING I'VE EVER *HEARD!* THE DOCTRINE OF THE *TRINITY* IS VITAL TO YOUR SPIRITUAL *WELL-BEING!* TO *CUT IT OUT* WOULD BE LIKE REMOVING YOUR *HEART!!*

FUNNY YOU SHOULD MENTION THAT!

5

ASK DR. DOCTRINE

I'M NOT *REALLY* A DOCTOR, BUT I *PLAY* ONE IN A *COMIC BOOK!*

DEAR DOC, IS THE DOCTRINE OF THE TRINITY IN THE BIBLE?

GOOD *QUESTION!*

YES, THE DOCTRINE OF THE *TRINITY* -- THAT GOD IS *FATHER, SON* AND *HOLY SPIRIT* -- IS *PROFOUNDLY* BIBLICAL.

SO IT'S *IN* THE BIBLE. BUT THE QUESTION IS, IS IT *BLATANT* OR *LATENT* IN THE BOOK?

NOW IF IT WERE *BLATANTLY* IN THERE, WE WOULD EXPECT TO FIND A FEW CLEAR *VERSES* TO QUOTE:

LIKE, "GOD IS THE *TRINITY*," ROMANS 8:40.

OR, "THERE ARE THREE *PERSONS* IN GOD'S ONE *ESSENCE*," EPHESIANS 6:25.

BUT OF COURSE THAT'S *NOT* HOW IT IS. THE WORD "*TRINITY*" IS NOT TO BE FOUND *ANYWHERE* IN THE BIBLE.

THEREFORE WE CAN'T SAY THAT THE DOCTRINE IS *BLATANT* IN SCRIPTURE.

BUT IT IS DEFINITELY *LATENT* IN THE BIBLE!

ALL THE EVIDENCE IS RIGHT THERE:

GOD IS *ONE!*

BUT *JESUS* IS GOD THE *SON!*

AND THE *SPIRIT* IS GOD!

THE *ONLY* WAY TO PUT ALL THESE IDEAS *TOGETHER* IN ONE *MIND*, WITHOUT BEING *IRRATIONAL*, IS TO BELIEVE THAT GOD IS THE *TRINITY!*

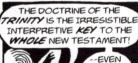

THE DOCTRINE OF THE *TRINITY* IS THE IRRESISTIBLE INTERPRETIVE *KEY* TO THE *WHOLE* NEW TESTAMENT!

--EVEN THOUGH IT TOOK THE CHURCH *CENTURIES* TO PUT IT IN WRITING FORMALLY!

BUT WHEN WE *DID* GET AROUND TO PUTTING IT ON PAPER, WE GOT IT *RIGHT!*

THAT'S MY ANSWER!

9

JESUS' *BAPTISM* IN THE JORDAN BY JOHN IS ALSO AN *EASY* ONE TO FIGURE OUT, BECAUSE ALL *THREE* PERSONS SHOW UP *VERY CLEARLY!*

LOOK HERE:

THE *SON* IS, AS ALWAYS, THE MOST *OBVIOUS* ONE: HE'S RIGHT THERE IN THE WATER, AND JOHN IS BEARING WITNESS TO HIM.

RIGHT *NOW* HE'S THE ONE BEING *BAPTIZED*, BUT LATER ON, IN FACT, "*HE* IS THE ONE WHO WILL BAPTIZE *YOU* WITH THE *HOLY SPIRIT!*"

"THE HOLY SPIRIT DESCENDED ON HIM IN *BODILY* FORM LIKE A *DOVE*," ACCORDING TO LUKE. THE *SPIRIT* IS ON JESUS CHRIST LIKE *NOBODY* ELSE; AS HE SAID, "THE *SPIRIT OF THE LORD* IS UPON ME, BECAUSE HE HAS *ANOINTED* ME."

"*CHRIST*," BY THE WAY, MEANS "THE *ANOINTED* ONE."

THE *FATHER* IS NOT *VISIBLE* AT THIS EVENT, BUT IT'S VERY IMPORTANT THAT HE IS PRESENT AS A *VOICE* FROM HEAVEN WHICH DECLARES:

THIS IS MY BELOVED SON, IN WHOM I AM WELL PLEASED.

13

14

15

MEET THE THEOLOGIANS

JÜRGEN MOLTMANN
b. 1926

JÜRGEN MOLTMANN RETIRED IN 1994, AFTER A LONG AND FRUITFUL CAREER TEACHING THEOLOGY IN TÜBINGEN. HE HAS BEEN ONE OF THE BEST-KNOWN AND MOST RESPECTED OF THE THEOLOGIANS TO EMERGE FROM POST-WAR GERMANY. BECAUSE HE DID NOT HAVE A CHRISTIAN UP-BRINGING, HE ALWAYS FELT LIKE THE IDEAS IN THE BIBLE WERE WONDERFUL NEW DIS-COVERIES THAT HE WAS MAKING.

PRESSED INTO THE GERMAN MILITARY AS A TEEN-AGED BOY, MOLTMANN BECAME A PRISON-ER OF WAR FROM 1945-48. IN THE BRIT-ISH PRISON CAMP, HE BEGAN TO STUDY THE BIBLE, AND BECAME A CHRISTIAN. THIS EXPER-IENCE OF FINDING GOD IN THE MIDST OF A DESPERATE SITUATION OF IMPRISON-MENT AND SHAME GAVE MOLTMANN THE CENTRAL PASSION THAT SHAPES HIS THEOLOGY: GOD IS THE GOD OF HOPE.

MOLTMANN'S FIRST MAJOR BOOK, THE THEOLOGY OF HOPE, ARGUED THAT ESCHATOLOGY, THE DOCTRINE OF THE FINAL THINGS, WAS NOT SOMETHING TACKED ON TO THE END OF OUR BELIEFS BUT IS THE VERY HEART OF CHRISTIAN FAITH. THE KINGDOM OF GOD IS NOT A NEVER-NEVER LAND BUT THE REAL DESTINY OF THE WORLD THAT LIES IN OUR FUTURE AS GOD HAS PROMISED. WE FIND OURSELVES NOW BETWEEN THE PROMISE AND ITS FULFILLMENT, AND THE CONTRADICTION BETWEEN THE WORLD'S CURRENT CONDITION AND THE FUTURE GOD HAS PROMISED SHOULD MAKE US RESTLESS ENOUGH TO TAKE ACTION WITH THE KINGDOM IN VIEW.

THIS IS WHERE WE LIVE!

P R O M I S E   F U L F I L L M E N T

MOLTMANN THINKS OF THE CROSS AS THE EVENT IN WHICH GOD DECLARES SOLIDARITY WITH "THE GODLESS AND THE GODFORSAKEN;" THAT IS, WHERE GOD MANIFESTS HIS LOVE FOR SINNERS AND FOR SUFFERERS. BECAUSE THE FATHER FEELS THE LOSS OF THE SON, AND THE SON SUFFERS SEP-ARATION FROM THE FATHER, GOD KNOWS PAIN FROM THE INSIDE OUT. SO MOLTMANN SEES THE CROSS AS AN EVENT BETWEEN THE PERSONS OF THE TRINITY, IN WHICH WE ARE ALSO IMPLICATED.

THERE'S A WHOLE LOT GOING ON HERE!

AS HE REFLECTED MORE ON THE MEANING OF JESUS CHRIST'S LIFE HISTORY, MOLTMANN BEGAN PAYING MORE AND MORE ATTENTION TO THE ROLE OF THE HOLY SPIRIT. MOLTMANN CAME TO REALIZE THAT MANY THEOLOGIANS NEGLECT THINKING ABOUT THE HOLY SPIRIT AND THAT THIS HABIT OF IGNORING THE SPIRIT HAS IMPOVERISHED ALL OTHER AREAS OF THEOLOGY.

PRAISE FATHER, SON, AND.... UH... WHAT'S NEXT?

MOLTMANN HAS LEARNED TO PAY CLOSE ATTENTION TO THE DETAILS OF THE BIBLICAL STORY AND TO PRESS THE QUESTION OF WHAT THE EVENTS OF JESUS CHRIST'S LIFE MEAN; NOT ONLY WHAT THEY MEAN FOR US, BUT WHAT THEY MEAN FOR GOD. THE ONLY WAY TO ANSWER THAT QUESTION IS TO TRY TO DETECT WHAT IS HAPPENING IN THE LIFE OF JESUS BETWEEN THE FATHER, THE SON AND THE HOLY SPIRIT.

JESUS' HISTORY IS AS INCOMPRE-HENSIBLE WITHOUT THE ACTION OF THE *SPIRIT* AS IT WOULD BE WITHOUT THE GOD WHOM HE CALLED "MY *FATHER*," OR WITHOUT HIS ACTIVITY OUT OF THE EXISTENCE OF "THE *SON*."

Albrecht Dürer, The Trinity, 1511

How To Draw

THE TRINITY

ASK DR. DOCTRINE

HOUSE CALLS, NO PROBLEM!

DEAR DOC, DOES THE BIBLE COMMAND US NOT TO MAKE *ANY* IMAGES?

GOOD QUESTION!

ASK MOST PEOPLE WHAT THE BIBLE HAS TO SAY ABOUT *ART*, AND THE ONLY VERSE THEY CAN COME UP WITH IS THE COMMAND "THOU SHALT MAKE *NO* GRAVEN *IMAGES*."

IMAGES

BUT *NOBODY* --ASIDE FROM MAYBE THE AMISH-- TAKES THAT TO MEAN THAT WE SHOULDN'T MAKE *ANY* PICTURES AT ALL!

TO MOST PEOPLE IT'S *OBVIOUS* THAT THE CONTEXT OF THAT PROHIBITION IS THAT WE SHOULDN'T MAKE *ANY* IMAGES IN ORDER TO BOW DOWN AND *WORSHIP* THEM. --THIS WAS SOMETHING THE ISRAELITES HAD TROUBLE WITH...

SHHHHH! THE GOLDEN CALF IS A *JEALOUS* GOD!

AND IF YOU LOOK AT THE *BROADER* CONTEXT, THAT COMMAND IS GIVEN IN THE *SAME* BOOK IN WHICH GOD TELLS THE ARTISTS OF ISRAEL TO *DECORATE* HIS TABERNACLE WITH GOLD, DRAPERIES, NEEDLEWORK, CARVINGS AND SO ON!

AMONG OTHER THINGS, GOD INSTRUCTS THE ARTISTS TO MAKE PICTURES OF *FLOWERS, BELLS, FRUITS* AND EVEN *ANGELS!*

--EVER TRY GETTING AN *ANGEL* TO POSE FOR A PORTRAIT?

IN FACT, THE ARTISTS EVEN GET PERMISSION TO MAKE *ABSTRACT* ART AND TO *IMAGINE* THINGS THEY'VE NEVER SEEN IN NATURE. FOR INSTANCE, THEY ARE TO MAKE *POMEGRANATES* IN SEVERAL COLORS, INCLUDING *PURPLE* ONES!

--EVER TRY GETTING A PURPLE *POMEGRANATE* TO POSE FOR A PORTRAIT?

SO THE *REAL* ISSUE, IN *ART* AS IN *LIFE*, IS *WORSHIP!*

DO YOU WORSHIP YOUR OWN *CREATIVITY*, OR DO YOU WORSHIP *GOD CREATIVELY?*

THAT'S MY ANSWER!

20

21

HERE'S AN OBVIOUS WAY TO EXPRESS THE IDEA THAT WE ARE **CREATED** BY FATHER, SON AND HOLY SPIRIT:

DEPICT **THREE GUYS** SEATED SIDE-BY-SIDE ON **ONE THRONE**, IN THE ACT OF MAKING **ADAM** AND **EVE**.

THIS IS KIND OF A **TENDER** LITTLE IMAGE, DON'T YOU THINK? IT'S FROM A THIRD-CENTURY CHRISTIAN COFFIN.

Anonymous, ca. 1515, Baden in Vienna

ONE THING I NOTICE IS THAT THE THREE MEN ON THE THRONE OFTEN LOOK THE **SAME: IDENTICAL TRIPLETS!**

YOU CAN TELL THEM APART BY CERTAIN SYMBOLS: CHRIST MAY HAVE **WOUNDS**, OR THE SPIRIT IN THIS CASE HAS A **LEAFY BRANCH** TO SHOW THAT HE'S "THE **GIVER OF LIFE**," AS THE NICENE CREED SAYS.

BUT IF THEY LOOK **IDENTICAL**, IT CAN SUGGEST THAT THEY'RE **INTERCHANGEABLE**, AND THAT'S CERTAINLY **NOT TRUE!** THE FATHER IS **NOT** THE SON, AND THE SON IS **NOT** THE HOLY SPIRIT.

LOOK AT **THIS** ONE: THE THREE BECOME SO IDENTICAL THAT THEY JUST **SIT** THERE SIDE BY SIDE, IMPOSSIBLE TO **TELL APART**...

...BUT IF THE **SON** IS ON THE **THRONE** IN HEAVEN, THEN **WHO** IS **THIS** ON THE **CROSS?**

THERE **MUST** BE A BETTER WAY FOR US TO IMAGINE THE TRINITY.

Luca di Tommè, Trinity and Crucifixion, 1360

HERE'S A SOLUTION: THIS ARTIST PAINTED *EACH* PERSON WITH A RECOGNIZABLE FACE, *DIFFERENT* FROM EACH OTHER!

WHICH IS *KIND OF* NICE...

Anonymous, ca. 1581, Soria

BUT *HOW* ON EARTH DOES HE KNOW THAT THE HOLY SPIRIT IS A *CURLY-HEADED YOUNG MAN* OR WHAT KIND OF *FACIAL HAIR* GOD THE FATHER HAS? THE MORE YOU THINK ABOUT IT, THE WEIRDER THE IDEA GETS...

THIS PAINTER PLAYED IT *SAFER*: WHAT WE *KNOW* FOR SURE ABOUT GOD THE FATHER IS THAT WHOEVER HAS SEEN THE *SON* HAS SEEN THE *FATHER.*

--SO HE MADE THEM LOOK LIKE *TWINS!*

Anonymous, from the Breviario Grimani, ca. 1515

AND HE PLAYED IT SAFE WITH THE *HOLY SPIRIT,* TOO: HE PAINTED HIM AS A *DOVE* INSTEAD OF AS YOUNG MR. CURLY-HEAD.

ONE PROBLEM WITH ALL THIS "THREE GUYS ON A THRONE" ART IS THAT IT SHOWS ALL THE *THREE* PERSONS, BUT CAN'T REALLY SHOW HOW THEY ARE *ONE IN ESSENCE.*

HERE'S A STRAIGHT-FORWARD ATTEMPT TO SHOW THEIR UNITY: THEY HAVE *THREE HEADS* BUT SHARE *ONE CROWN!*

HA!

Anonymous, ca. 1288, Spain

23

OR, TO TAKE THE "UNITY" IMAGE ONE STEP *FURTHER*, THIS ARTIST *LINKED* THEM --IN ONE COMMON *GARMENT!*

Anonymous, 14th c., France

WHICH IS KIND OF *ODD*, BUT IN A *CHARMING* WAY, I THINK!

BUT IF THAT'S *STILL* TOO SEPARATE FOR YOU, HOW ABOUT *THIS: ONE BODY* WITH *THREE HEADS! YIKES!*

THE *SON* AND THE *SPIRIT* LOOK LIKE SOME KIND OF *SHOULDER PADS* THAT THE FATHER IS WEARING!

Anonymous, 16th c., France

WEIRD ENOUGH FOR YOU YET? WELL, HANG ON TO YOUR THREE HATS, BECAUSE IT KEEPS GOING...

IN THE *ULTIMATE* ATTEMPT TO SHOW THE *UNITY* OF THE THREE PERSONS, SEVERAL ARTISTS STARTED SHOWING GOD AS HAVING *ONE HEAD* WITH *THREE SEPARATE FACES!!*

Andrea del Sarto, Trinity, 1519

SOMETIMES WITH *SIX* EYES, SOMETIMES WITH *FOUR!*

Anon., 16th c., France

24

17th c., Spanish

15th c., France

16th c., France

12th c., Spain

HERE'S A GOOD CHANCE TO SEE HOW PEOPLE IN THE MIDDLE AGES ACTUALLY *USED* THESE IMAGES IN THEIR PRAYER-LIVES. THE NEXT FIVE PICTURES WE'LL BE LOOKING AT COME FROM ONE PLACE: CATHERINE OF CLEVES' *"BOOK OF HOURS,"* A FOURTEENTH-CENTURY WORK.

A *"BOOK OF HOURS"* WAS A MEDIEVAL DEVOTIONAL BOOK; THEY INCLUDED PARTS OF SCRIPTURE, SOME PRAYERS AND ALSO *PICTURES!* PEOPLE USED THEM FOR THEIR "QUIET TIMES."

THE SECTION ON THE *TRINITY* STARTS OUT WITH AN IMAGE WE'VE SEEN *BEFORE: THREE* MEN SEATED ON *ONE* THRONE.

THE *FATHER* HOLDS THE GLOBE THAT SYMBOLIZES ALL OF CREATION; THE *SON* HAS A CROSS-SHAPE IN HIS HALO; AND THAT MEANS THE MAN WEARING THE WHITE GOWN MUST BE THE *HOLY SPIRIT!*

CLEAR ENOUGH, RIGHT?

WE'VE ALREADY SEEN SOME OF THE *PROBLEMS* WITH THIS KIND OF A PAINTING: IT SHOWS US THREE VERY *DISTINCT* PEOPLE, BUT CAN'T CAPTURE THEIR *UNITY* CLEARLY.

ALSO, IT PRESUMES TO KNOW WHAT THE *FATHER* AND *SPIRIT* LOOK LIKE, AND THAT THEY ARE SOMEHOW *MALE*, AND OF A CERTAIN *AGE!*

MAYBE CATHERINE OF CLEVES, WHOEVER SHE WAS, DIDN'T HAVE A *PROBLEM* WITH THAT, BE- CAUSE SHE UNDERSTOOD THAT THIS WASN'T SUPPOSED TO BE A *PHOTOGRAPH* OF WHAT THE TRINITY *"LOOKS LIKE."* KIND OF LIKE THE THREE BUNNIES, IT'S JUST A *REMINDER* OF WHAT WE ALREADY KNOW...

ANYWAY, WE GET TO *TURN* THE *PAGE* AND SEE THE *NEXT* WAY OF LOOKING AT THE *TRINITY!*

THE NEXT PICTURE IS THE SAME SCENE, BUT NOW THE SON HAS **STEPPED DOWN** FROM THE THRONE AND IS **KNEELING** BEFORE THE **FATHER:** THIS IMAGE IS CALLED "THE SENDING OF THE SON."

THE FATHER IS **BLESSING** THE SON WITH ONE HAND AND HANDING HIM THE **CROSS** WITH THE OTHER. AS THE SON **ACCEPTS** THE CROSS, THE HOLY SPIRIT PLACES A HAND ON HIS SHOULDER TO **STRENGTHEN** AND **COMFORT** HIM.

BY LETTING US SEE A **PICTURE** OF JESUS CONSENTING TO DO WHATEVER IS NECESSARY FOR OUR **SALVATION,** THE ARTIST HELPS US UNDERSTAND THE **SELF-EMPTYING** OF GOD THE SON: "WHO, BEING **GOD** BY NATURE, DID NOT **CLING** TO THIS STATUS BUT MADE HIMSELF **NOTHING** AND TOOK ON HIMSELF THE FORM OF A **SERVANT.**" --PHILIPPIANS 2.

WHERE IS THIS HAPPENING? WHAT IS THIS **THRONE ROOM** WE'RE LOOKING INTO? IT'S A GLIMPSE INTO THE VERY **HEART** OF GOD...

IT'S ALSO A WAY OF PICTURING THAT FAMOUS VERSE, JOHN 3:16: **GOD** --MEANING GOD THE **FATHER**-- LOVED THE WORLD **SO MUCH** THAT HE **GAVE** HIS ONLY SON SO THAT THOSE WHO BELIEVE IN HIM MAY NOT PERISH...

AND AT THE SAME TIME IT TOOK PLACE IN THE **LIFE OF JESUS** AMONG US. CHANGE THE BACKGROUND, AND THIS **COULD** BE AN IMAGINATIVE PORTRAYAL OF JESUS' **PRAYER** IN THE GARDEN OF **GETHSEMANE!**

IT **HELPS** US TO REMEMBER THAT THE SON IS CARRYING OUT THE **MISSION** HE WAS SENT ON BY HIS FATHER... AND **OUR** FATHER!

27

ON THE *NEXT* PAGE IN CATHERINE'S LITTLE BOOK, WE SEE THE SON OF GOD COMING INTO THE WORLD CARRYING HIS *DESTINY* WITH HIM: THE *CROSS*, WHICH HE LOOKS LIKE HE'S ABOUT TO *PLANT* ON ONE OF THE LUSH GREEN HILLS.

JESUS IS *SENT* BY THE *FATHER* AND *ACCOMPANIED* BY THE *SPIRIT*, SO WHEN HE COMES TO OUR TURF, IT MEANS THE *HOLY TRINITY* IS DOING *BUSINESS* WITH US!

THIS PICTURE SYMBOLIZES THE *INCARNATION*, WHEN GOD THE SON ACTUALLY TOOK HIS *STAND* WITHIN THE CREATED WORLD, BECOMING A HUMAN TO SAVE US!

IT'S KIND OF THE *FLIP-SIDE* OF THE PREVIOUS PAGE, BECAUSE *BOTH* PICTURES SHOW THE *SAME* EVENT.

THE ARTIST WANTS US TO GET THE *POINT*: THE TWO THINGS GO *TOGETHER* AS TWO ASPECTS OF *ONE* EVENT.

BUT WHILE THE *"HEAVENLY THRONE ROOM"* PICTURE IS AN IMAGE OF THE *ETERNAL* GOD'S *INTERIOR* LIFE, THIS *"GREEN HILLS"* PAINTING IS A REFERENCE TO AN EVENT IN OUR OWN TIME AND SPACE!

CHRIST AMONG US *IS* THE REVELATION OF *GOD'S* INNER *LIFE*!

ON THE *NEXT* PAGE, CATHERINE'S BOOK SHOWS US *ANOTHER* WAY OF VISUALIZING THE *TRINITY*, THIS TIME WITH THE *CROSS* ITSELF RIGHT IN THE MIDDLE!

THIS WAY OF PICTURING THE TRINITY BECAME VERY *POPULAR*. IT CAME TO BE CALLED "THE *THRONE OF GRACE*."

GOD THE *FATHER*, SEATED ON A THRONE, HOLDS THE *CROSS-BAR* IN HIS HANDS. THE *SON* HANGS ON THE CROSS, AND THE *SPIRIT*, PICTURED AS A DOVE, FLIES BETWEEN THEM.

HERE'S A NICE TOUCH: THE *GLOBE* WHICH THE FATHER USUALLY *HOLDS* IS NOW AT THE FOOT OF THE *CROSS*...

GOD THE FATHER IS STILL *IN TOUCH* WITH CREATION, BUT NOW IT'S THROUGH THE *CRUCIFIED SON* OF GOD THAT HE DEALS WITH THE WORLD.

ANOTHER DETAIL TO NOTICE IS THE *POSITION* OF THE *SPIRIT*: THIS ARTIST DECIDED THAT THE DOVE SHOULD BE SHOWN FLYING *FROM* JESUS *TO* THE FATHER. *WHY*?

POSSIBLY TO REPRESENT JESUS' *LAST* WORDS: "FATHER, INTO *YOUR HANDS* I COMMEND *MY SPIRIT*," AFTER WHICH HE BREATHED HIS FINAL *BREATH*.

BUT *MANY* ARTISTS SHOW THE DOVE IN OTHER WAYS: FLYING *FROM* THE FATHER *TO* THE SON, OR HOVERING *BETWEEN* THEM WITH ONE WINGTIP TOUCHING *EACH*, OR EVEN UP *ABOVE* THE FATHER'S HEAD.

WHAT DOES ALL *THIS* MEAN? YOU TELL *ME*!

29

WELL, THAT'S ENOUGH TIME TO SPEND WITH *ONE* ARTIST! I WANT TO *FINISH UP* BY SHOWING THAT THERE ARE *OTHER* WAYS TO PICTURE THE TRINITY, WITHOUT HAVING TO RESORT TO THE "THREE MEN ON A THRONE" CONVENTION.

IN THE EASTERN CHURCH, ARTISTS *REFUSED* TO PAINT GOD THE FATHER!

INSTEAD, THEY LOOKED FOR *CLUES* IN THE BIBLE OF A *SAFER* WAY TO SHOW THE THREE PERSONS...

ONE THING THEY CAME UP WITH WAS THE STORY OF THE 3 ANGELS WHO CAME TO ABRAHAM AND FORE-TOLD THE BIRTH OF ISAAC.

Anon., ca. 1182, Monreale

GENESIS SAYS: "*THE LORD* APPEARED TO ABRAHAM... HE LOOKED UP AND SAW *THREE MEN.*" NOW THIS IS REALLY A *VERY* MYSTERIOUS PASSAGE, BUT THE CHURCH TOOK IT AS A *FORE-SHADOWING* OF THE TRINITY, AND ARTISTS SAW THEIR CHANCE TO MAKE AN *ICON* OF THE TRINITY WITHOUT BEING IRREVERENT.

Andrei Rublev, 1425

THIS FAMOUS VERSION OF THE SCENE HAS *STRIPPED* IT DOWN TO THE BARE MINIMUM: THREE *GRACEFUL ANGELS,* SEATED AT A COMMON *MEAL.* --KIND OF NICE, I THINK. *MYSTERIOUS* AND *EVOCATIVE...*

31

BUT IF I *HAD* TO CHOOSE THE *BEST*, SAFEST, MOST *REVERENT* WAY OF REPRESENTING THE TRINITY VISUALLY, I WOULDN'T *HESITATE* ONE SECOND: IT'S *DEFINITELY* THE IMAGE OF THE *BAPTISM* OF JESUS!

5TH C., RAVENNA

IT'S PROBABLY THE *OLDEST* WAY, TOO ... THIS SMUDGY PICTURE WAS FOUND IN THE CATACOMBS. THE *DOVE* IS BARELY VISIBLE.

IT BECAME A VERY POPULAR IMAGE TO USE IN *BAPTISTRIES*: IT ONLY MAKES SENSE...

WHEN A CHRISTIAN IS BEING *BAPTIZED* IN THE *NAME* OF THE FATHER, SON AND HOLY SPIRIT, WE SHOULD REMEMBER THE BAPTISM OF JESUS CHRIST, WHERE THE *SPIRIT* CAME TO REST ON HIM, AND THE FATHER DE-CLARED, "THIS IS MY *BELOVED SON!*"

NOTICE HOW IN THIS PICTURE JESUS SLIPS HIS HAND OUT OF THE WATER TO OFFER A *BLESS-ING* --JUST TO SHOW THAT HE'S NOT HERE TO REPENT OF HIS *OWN* SINS BUT TO DELIVER *US* FROM *OURS!*

13th c., Venice

32

AT CHRIST'S BAPTISM, ALL THREE *PERSONS* ARE *PRESENT* AND EASY TO *IDENTIFY*. AND THERE'S NO NEED TO *MAKE UP* SOME IDEA OF WHAT THEY *LOOK* LIKE!

Anon., 10th c.

IN THE SIMPLEST FORM, THE *FATHER* IS INDICATED BY A SYMBOLIC *HAND*...

THE *SPIRIT* BY A DESCENDING *DOVE*...

AND THE *SON*, OF COURSE, IS THE *VISIBLE, TANGIBLE,* AND FULLY *INCARNATE* LORD JESUS CHRIST!

SO *THERE* YOU HAVE IT: THE *HIGH* POINTS AND *LOW* POINTS OF CHRISTIAN ART'S ATTEMPTS TO MAKE AN *IMAGE* OF THE *TRINITY*. NO PICTURE IS *PERFECT*, BUT MOST OF THEM ARE *HELPFUL!*

IT SEEMS TO ME THAT THE MORE THE ARTISTS GET *OBSESSED* WITH THE NUMBER *THREE*, THE MORE *PROBLEMATIC* THEIR ART GETS.

--AND THE MORE THEY PAY ATTENTION TO THE ACTUAL *LIFE* AND *HISTORY* OF JESUS CHRIST, THE MORE *MEANINGFUL* THEIR IMAGES BECOME.

--COME TO *THINK* OF IT, THAT'S A *LOT* LIKE LIVING THE CHRISTIAN *LIFE*, ISN'T IT?

GREGORY of NAZIANZUS

330-390 GREGORY WAS BORN INTO A STRONG CHRISTIAN FAMILY IN ASIA MINOR. HIS MOM HAD A REPUTATION FOR HOLINESS, AND HIS DAD WAS A BISHOP. THEY DEDICATED GREGORY TO GOD BEFORE HE WAS BORN AND PAID FOR HIM TO HAVE A SOLID EDUCATION AT THE BEST SCHOOLS IN THE EMPIRE.

GREGORY LOVED STUDYING AND WAS DRAWN TO THE IDEA OF A QUIET LIFE OF SIMPLICITY, MEDITATION ON THE BIBLE AND PRAYER. BUT HIS COLLEGE ROOMMATE AND BEST PAL, BASIL THE GREAT, NEEDED GREGORY'S HELP TO CARRY OUT SOME BIG PLANS. ALL HIS LIFE BASIL KEPT TALKING GREGORY INTO TAKING ON DEMANDING NEW ASSIGNMENTS.

FOR EXAMPLE, GREGORY WAS SERVING HIS TERM AS BISHOP OF CONSTANTINOPLE IN THE YEAR 381 WHEN THE SECOND ECUMENICAL COUNCIL MET THERE. THIS WAS THE COUNCIL WHERE THE NICENE CREED WAS PUT INTO THE FINAL FORM IN WHICH IT IS STILL RECITED TODAY ALL OVER THE WORLD.

YE OLDE NICENE CREEDE

THERE WERE HERETICS AT THIS TIME WHO TAUGHT THAT THE HOLY SPIRIT SHOULD NOT BE THOUGHT OF AS DIVINE BUT ONLY AS A CREATURE OR POWER. THE NICENE CREED REFUTES THAT HERESY, SAYING THAT THE SPIRIT IS "LORD AND GIVER OF LIFE." GREGORY WANTED TO GO FURTHER THAN THAT AND SAY QUITE BLUNTLY THAT THE SPIRIT IS SIMPLY DIVINE: OF THE SAME ESSENCE AS GOD.

ANOTHER DANGEROUS IDEA FLOATING AROUND WAS THAT JESUS DIDN'T HAVE A HUMAN SOUL, BUT WAS JUST "GOD IN A BOD." GREGORY DISAGREED:

> THAT WHICH IS NOT *ASSUMED* IS NOT *HEALED!*

WHICH MEANS WHAT?

> IT MEANS THAT JESUS *SAVES* US BY *TAKING ON* ALL THAT MAKES US WHAT WE ARE. IF HE DIDN'T *HAVE* A SOUL, HE DIDN'T SAVE *MINE!*

GREGORY EARNED SOME GREAT NICKNAMES: HE WAS SUCH A TALENTED ORATOR THAT HE WAS CALLED "THE CHRISTIAN DEMOSTHENES." OTHERS CALLED HIM "THE CANTOR OF THE TRINITY" BECAUSE HIS DOCTRINE WAS AS CLEAR AND COMPELLING AS A SONG. IN FACT, HIS TEACHING WAS SO AUTHORITATIVE THAT HE IS USUALLY KNOWN SIMPLY AS: GREGORY THE THEOLOGIAN.

> WHEN I SAY *GOD*, WHAT I MEAN IS *FATHER, SON* AND *HOLY SPIRIT!*

TRINITY MATH

ASK DR. DOCTRINE

I'M JUST *ONE* DOC, NOT A *PAIR* O'DOCS!

DEAR DOC, DO WE AS CHRISTIANS BELIEVE IN PARADOXES AND CONTRADICTIONS?

GOOD QUESTION!

FIRST OF ALL, LET'S *SEPARATE* THESE TWO TERMS, BECAUSE THEY'RE *NOT* THE SAME THING AT ALL!

PARADOX

CONTRADICTION

A *PARADOX* IS AN *APPARENT* CONTRADICTION, OR SOMETHING THAT *LOOKS* ILLOGICAL BUT REALLY ISN'T.

BUT A *CONTRADICTION* IS SOMETHING THAT JUST DOESN'T MAKE SENSE *AT ALL, EVER,* TO *ANYONE.*

LIKE "*APPLES* ARE *ORANGES.*" THERE'S NO WAY TO *BELIEVE* THAT, BECAUSE YOU CAN'T REALLY *THINK* IT COHERENTLY.

NOW, WE BELIEVE ALL *KINDS* OF THINGS THAT WE DON'T FULLY UNDERSTAND, AND WE JUST HAVE TO *ACCEPT* SOME OF THEM AS PARADOXES, OR THINGS WE MAY UNDERSTAND *LATER.*

BUT WALKING BY *FAITH* DOES *NOT* MEAN BELIEVING THINGS THAT AREN'T TRUE, OR THAT ARE *LOGICALLY* IMPOSSIBLE, OR JUST PLAIN *CRAZY.*

OUR FAITH IS IN *GOD,* WHO CANNOT *LIE.* SO IF *GOD* WERE TO SAY THAT *APPLES* ARE *ORANGES,* IT WOULD BE BECAUSE THEY REALLY REALLY *ARE,* AND WE'LL UNDERSTAND IT BETTER BY AND BY! MAKE SENSE? IT SHOULD!

THAT'S MY ANSWER!

36

37

IT'S REALLY *EMBARASSING* TO HAVE PEOPLE THINK YOUR BELIEFS ARE *ILLOGICAL* AND INDEFENSIBLE.

HECK, I GET THAT ALL THE *TIME!* EVERY TIME I TRY TO EXPLAIN ABOUT HOW *FINGERNAILS* ARE REALLY A TYPE OF *FUNGUS*--

MAYBE THE BEST PLACE TO *START* ISN'T WITH THIS *ALGEBRAIC* APPROACH, SCHWARTZ!

WHAT? BUT ISN'T *THAT* THE *PROBLEM:* "HOW CAN THREE BE *ONE?* "

WELL, NOT *REALLY.*

THE "*PROBLEM*" BEHIND THE TRINITY IS THE CHRISTIAN BELIEF THAT *JESUS* IS THE *SON OF GOD.*

--IF YOU CALL THAT A *PROBLEM.*

EXACTLY!

THE FIRST CHRISTIANS HAD TO ANSWER THE QUESTION, HOW CAN YOU BELIEVE JESUS IS *GOD,* AND STILL BE *MONOTHEISTS?*

YEAH, THAT'S A *TOUGH* ONE: IT'S LIKE WE'RE SAYING "THERE'S ONLY *ONE* GOD, BUT JESUS IS *ALSO* GOD."

RIGHT. AND THERE'S NO GETTING *AROUND* THE QUESTION OF *HOW* TO PUT THOSE TWO IDEAS TOGETHER, BECAUSE THEY'RE *BOTH* CLEARLY TAUGHT IN THE *BIBLE*.

THE EARLY CHURCH TALKED IT OVER FOR A WHILE, AND FINALLY DECIDED THAT WE NEED TO DISTINGUISH BETWEEN *WHAT* JESUS IS AND *WHO* JESUS IS.

WHAT JESUS IS, IS *GOD* IN ESSENCE. BUT *WHO* JESUS IS, IS THE *SON OF GOD*, OR *GOD THE SON*.

--AND THE SAME DISTINCTION APPLIES TO GOD THE FATHER: *WHAT* HE IS IS *GOD*, BUT *WHO* HE IS IS THE *FATHER OF JESUS* CHRIST.

HEY! *THAT* MEANS THAT JESUS AND GOD THE FATHER ARE THE SAME *WHAT*, BUT TWO DIFFERENT *WHO*S!

EXACTLY! SO ADD THE *HOLY SPIRIT*, AND YOU'VE GOT THE *TRINITY*: THREE *WHO*S AND ONE *WHAT*!

ONE *WHAT*?

RIGHT!

NO, I MEAN ONE *WHAT*?

THAT'S WHAT WE'RE SAYING.

NOW CUT THAT OUT!! I'M TRYING TO ASK, ONE *WHAT? WHAT* IS GOD *ONE* OF?

OH. SORRY.

WELL, THAT'S HARD TO SAY. *IMPOSSIBLE* TO SAY, REALLY. I MEAN, WHO *KNOWS* WHAT GOD IS? ONE *GOD.* ONE *BEING,* ONE *ESSENCE. ONE.* GOD IS GOD.

BUT IN ADDITION TO BEING ONE *WHAT,* OR ONE *GOD,* GOD IS ALSO THREE *WHO*s, OR THREE *PERSONS.* --AND WE KNOW *THAT* BECAUSE THE APOSTLES *MET* JESUS CHRIST --GOD *WITH* US-- WHO PRAYED TO GOD AS HIS FATHER --GOD *ABOVE*-- AND GAVE THE SPIRIT --GOD *WITHIN* US! THREE *WHO*S!

THAT'S WHY THE *3=1* PROBLEM ISN'T *REALLY* THE MAIN POINT. WE BELIEVE THAT GOD IS ONE *BEING,* BUT THREE *PERSONS.*

OH, I *GET* IT! IT'S *NOT* AS IF WE'RE SAYING GOD IS *ONE BEING* AND AT THE SAME TIME *THREE* BEINGS!

--OR *ONE PERSON* AND AT THE SAME TIME *THREE* PERSONS! THAT WOULD JUST BE *ILLOGICAL* AND IMPOSSIBLE TO BELIEVE WITHOUT ABSURDITY.

SO THE TRINITY ISN'T A *MYSTERY* AT *ALL,* THEN?

WHOA! THE *TRINITY* IS *GOD,* AND GOD IS AN *ABSOLUTE* MYSTERY! WE CAN *KNOW* AND *LOVE* HIM, BUT WE CAN *NEVER* GET HIM *FIGURED OUT* AND *PINNED DOWN!*

BUT THAT'S *DIFFERENT* FROM SAYING THAT WHAT WE *BELIEVE* ABOUT GOD CAN BE *NONSENSE*. *OUR* SENTENCES ABOUT *GOD* HAVE TO *MAKE SENSE*, JUST LIKE EVERYBODY ELSE'S.

WE CAN'T JUST SAY, "GOD IS A *MYSTERY*, SO IT'S NO WONDER YOU DON'T UNDERSTAND AND WHEN I SAY THAT GOD IS *FIVE* AND YET *NINE* BEINGS, AND DRIVES A *CAR* YET *WALKS* AT THE SAME TIME."

WHY *NOT?* MAKES SENSE TO *ME!*

UH...

UMMM....

...

SO LET ME SEE IF I'VE GOT THIS *STRAIGHT:* WE CAN HAVE A *PERSONAL* RELATIONSHIP WITH THIS GOD WHO IS ONE *WHAT* AND THREE *WHO*S.

YES. BUT REMEMBER, YOU HAVE A PERSONAL *RELATIONSHIP* WITH A *WHO*, NOT A *WHAT*. AND *THAT* MEANS THAT COMING TO KNOW *GOD* INVOLVES COMING TO KNOW THE *FATHER*, THE *SON* AND THE *HOLY SPIRIT*.

OH! IT'S ALMOST LIKE I HAVE *THREE* PERSONAL RELATIONSHIPS WITH GOD, INSTEAD OF JUST *ONE!*

WELL YEAH, SORT OF. OR SINCE THE THREE ARE *INSEPARABLE*, WE HAVE *ONE* RELATIONSHIP WITH THE ONE, *THREE-PERSONED* GOD!

SEE, WE TALK ABOUT A *PERSONAL GOD*, BUT IN FACT GOD IS NOT *JUST* PERSONAL; HE'S FAR *MORE* THAN THAT.

HEY, YOU'RE GIVING ME THE *CREEPS!* IS THIS GOING TO BE THAT "GOD IS THE *GROUND* OF BEING, AND I DROP INTO HIM LIKE A RAINDROP INTO THE *OCEAN*" KIND OF JUNK?

YEAH, WHAT'S UP WITH *THAT?*

NO NO NO, I SAID GOD IS *MORE* THAN PERSONAL, NOT *LESS!* THAT "OCEAN" STUFF IS *IM*-PERSONAL, BUT WHAT WE BELIEVE IS THAT GOD IS *SUPER*-PERSONAL, OR *TRI-PERSONAL!* FATHER, SON AND SPIRIT!

GREETINGS, FELLOW SHEEP! I COULDN'T HELP *OVERHEARING*, AND I THINK I MIGHT BE ABLE TO HELP *CLARIFY* THIS PROBLEM WITH AN *ANALOGY* OR TWO!

OH, HI *THEO!* WELL, GO AHEAD, BUT REMEMBER THAT *ALL* ANALOGIES TO GOD ARE BOUND TO BE VERY *LIMITED* IN HOW MUCH THEY CAN HELP....

WELL, IT SEEMS TO ME THAT GOD IS THREE AND YET ONE, LIKE H_2O CAN BE *STEAM, WATER* OR *ICE*, AND YET STILL REMAIN HYDROGEN AND OXYGEN.

UM, WELL, THAT'S O*KAY*, BUT GOD DOESN'T *TURN INTO* FATHER, SON, AND SPIRIT ONE *AFTER* THE OTHER. HE'S *ALREADY*--

--OR PERHAPS THE FATHER AND THE SON ARE TWO *HYDROGENS*, AND THE HOLY SPIRIT IS THE *OXYGEN!*

WELL, UH, OKAY, BUT IT'S NOT THAT THERE ARE THREE *PARTS* OF GOD! JESUS IS NOT THE *"SON" PART* OF GOD, HE'S GOD THE SON, *INDIVISIBLY!*

HEY! *I* GOT AN ANALOGY! *PARK, REVERSE* AND *NEUTRAL*, AND YET IT'S NOT *THREE TRANSMISSIONS* BUT *ONE!*

OR PERHAPS THE MODEL OF THREE *DIMENSIONS* IN ONE PHYSICAL *SPACE* IS MORE APPROPRIATE...

NO, I THINK *BOTH* OF THOSE ANALOGIES ARE *FLAWED...*

HEY HEY HEY! HOW ABOUT THAT *NAPOLEON* ICE CREAM, WHERE IT'S *CHOCOLATE,* AND *VANILLA,* AND *STRAWBERRY,* BUT IT COMES IN *ONE* BOX, AND IT'S ALL *ONE* BLOCK OF *ICE CREAM!* NOW *THERE'S* A MYSTERY FOR YOU, MAN!

UH...

THE BODY, SOUL AND SPIRIT HAVE A *TRIPARTITE* STRUCTURE AS WELL...

--*BANANAS* COME APART INTO THREE LITTLE WEDGES! *ONE* BANANA!

THE THREE *LIBERAL ARTS:* GRAMMATICA, DIALECTICA AND RHETORICA: TOGETHER THEY ARE *ONE EDUCATION.*

...AND THEY GOT LITTLE TINY *SEEDS!*

--OR LIKE THAT *GOOBER-GRAPE* PEANUT BUTTER YOU CAN BUY. HOW DO THEY *DO* THAT, ANYWAY? AND WHERE'S THE *HOLY SPIRIT?* THE *JAR?* OR IS THAT THE *FATHER?*

HEY, THE LADY AT THE *STORE* ASKED ME: *"CASH, CHECK* OR *CHARGE?"* I DO BELIEVE SHE WAS TRYING TO *WITNESS* TO ME!

AH YES, THE *ECONOMIC* TRINITY!

-- BUT THEN SHE SAID, *"PAPER OR PLASTIC?"*

MOST LIKELY A REFERENCE TO THE TWO NATURES OF *CHRIST...*

43

AUGUSTINE of Hippo

354-430

AURELIUS AUGUSTINUS, BISHOP OF THE CITY OF HIPPO IN NORTH AFRICA, IS UNDOUBTEDLY ONE OF THE MOST INFLUENTIAL THINKERS IN CHRISTIAN HISTORY. IN HIS WORKS HE SUMMED UP ALL THE THEOLOGY OF HIS PREDECESSORS IN AN ENCYCLOPEDIC WAY, AND THROUGH HIS ORIGINALITY AND INSIGHT HE HAS INFLUENCED EVERY ASPECT OF THE WESTERN CHURCH'S LIFE AND THOUGHT.

HIS CONFESSIONS, IN WHICH HE REFLECTS ON HIS LIFE BY WRITING OUT A LONG, MEDITATIVE PRAYER TO GOD, IS THE FIRST REALLY INTROSPECTIVE AUTOBIOGRAPHY. AUGUSTINE EXAMINED HIS EXPERIENCES SO CAREFULLY AND SO PRAYERFULLY THAT HE WAS ABLE TO SEE THE FULL HORROR OF ORIGINAL SIN IN A CHILDHOOD PRANK IN WHICH HE AND HIS FRIENDS STOLE PEARS JUST FOR THE FUN OF STEALING. THEY GAVE THE PEARS TO PIGS.

AN ADULT CONVERT TO THE FAITH, AUGUSTINE TOOK THE CHURCH'S DOCTRINES AS A SACRED TRUST, WHICH IT WAS HIS TASK TO LEARN SO HE COULD TEACH THEM TO OTHERS. HE WRESTLED WITH EACH TEACHING UNTIL IT MADE SENSE TO HIM. ONCE WHILE HE WAS WRITING HIS BOOK ABOUT THE TRINITY, HE TOOK A WALK AND CAME ACROSS A CHILD TRYING TO POUR THE OCEAN INTO A LITTLE HOLE HE HAD DUG IN THE SAND...

HEY, KID! YOU CAN'T FIT THE WHOLE OCEAN IN THERE! I SHOULD KNOW, I'M A VERY SMART GUY WHO'S WRITING A BOOK ON THE TRIN-- HEY, WAIT A MINUTE...

ONE OF AUGUSTINE'S MANY ORIGINAL CONTRIBUTIONS TO CHRISTIAN DOCTRINE WAS HIS ANALOGIES TO HELP UNDERSTAND THE TRINITY. HE ARGUED THAT SINCE WE ARE CREATED IN GOD'S IMAGE, THAT MUST MEAN THAT WE ARE IN THE IMAGE OF THE TRINITY, AND WE SHOULD BE ABLE TO USE THE TRACES OF THE TRINITY IN OUR OWN QUEST TO UNDERSTAND THE TRINITY OF GOD. INDEED, THE THREEFOLDNESS OF OUR MEMORY, UNDERSTANDING AND LOVE ARE ANALOGOUS TO GOD, AND ESPECIALLY WHEN IT IS GOD WHO WE ARE REMEMBERING, KNOWING AND LOVING.

AUGUSTINE LIVED DURING THE VERY END OF THE ROMAN EMPIRE, A DIFFICULT TIME. PAGANS BLAMED CHRISTIANS FOR THE FALL OF ROME, SAYING THAT THE ROMAN GODS WERE ANGRY AND WERE PUNISHING THE EMPIRE FOR TURNING TO THE GOD OF THE CHRISTIANS. TO REFUTE THIS ATTACK AUGUSTINE WROTE THE CITY OF GOD, IN WHICH HE ARGUED THAT EARTHLY KINGDOMS ARE BOUND TO FALL, BUT THE KINGDOM OF HEAVEN ENDURES.

THE KEYNOTE OF AUGUSTINE'S THOUGHT IS LOVE, A THEME WHICH HE DEVELOPED IN COUNTLESS WAYS. ABOVE ALL, HE NEVER FORGOT THAT HUMANS ARE CREATED BY GOD SO THAT WE CAN COME TO KNOW AND LOVE GOD ETERNALLY. THE NEED FOR GOD IS BUILT IN TO THE VERY CORE OF WHO WE ARE. PROBABLY THE MOST FAMOUS AUGUSTINE QUOTE, FROM HIS CONFESSIONS, SAYS EXACTLY THAT:

YOU HAVE MADE US FOR *YOURSELF*, OH LORD, AND OUR HEARTS ARE *RESTLESS* UNTIL THEY FIND THEIR REST IN *YOU*.

THEO & DEMPSEY'S WORD PAGE

IT'S A *GLOSSARY* OF *TERMINOLOGY* PERTINENT TO THE *THEMES* DISCUSSED IN THIS ISSUE!

IT'S A *WORD PAGE*, JUST LIKE IT *SAYS*, FOLKS!

TRINITY

THE WORD ITSELF IS *NOT* FOUND IN THE SCRIPTURES, BUT WAS INTRODUCED *LATER* AS AN *AID* FOR UNDERSTANDING THE BIBLE. THE GREEK TERM "*TRIAS*" WAS FIRST USED IN THE YEAR 170, AND THE LATIN FORM, "*TRINITAS*," WAS INTRODUCED CIRCA 200 A.D.

IT AIN'T IN THE BIBLE, BUT *THAT* DON'T MEAN IT'S NOT A BIBLICAL *IDEA*. IT GOES *WAAAAAY* BACK, AND MOST CHRISTIANS ARE *OKAY* WITH IT. SUITS ME!

TRITHEISM

TRITHEISM IS THE *HERESY* OF ASSERTING THAT THERE ARE *THREE* DIVINE BEINGS, ALL EQUAL AND INDEPENDENT OF EACH OTHER. FEW CHRISTIANS HAVE EVER FALLEN INTO THIS ERROR, BUT IT IS WORTH BEARING IN MIND THAT SUCH A VIEW EXISTS.

"*TRI*" MEANS *THREE*, "*THE*" IS SHORT FOR "*THE LORD*," AND AN "*-ISM*" IS ALWAYS SOME KIND OF A *DISEASE*. PUT THEM *TOGETHER* AND YOU'VE GOT "THE *DISEASE* OF THINKING THERE'S *THREE GODS*."

--THAT'S CALLED AN "*ETYMOLOGY*," WHICH MEANS "CUTTING UP *BUGS*."

MODALISM

MODALISM IS ANOTHER *HERESY*, WHICH PICTURES GOD AS *INTERNALLY* UNI-PERSONAL BUT ADMITS THAT HE *MANIFESTS* HIMSELF IN SUCH A WAY THAT *WE* SEE THE *APPEARANCE* OF THREE PERSONS.

SO LIKE, THERE'S THIS *ONE PERSON* NAMED *GOD*, AND HE PUTS ON A *MASK* AND SAYS "NOW I'M THE *FATHER*," THEN PUTS ON A *DIFFERENT* MASK AND SAYS, "*NOW* I'M THE *SON*." WELL, THAT'S JUST *CRAZY TALK!* HE'D HAVE TO BE A *VENTRILOQUIST*, OR ELSE HOW DO YOU EXPLAIN JESUS *PRAYING* TO HIS FATHER? HUH? ANSWER THAT, SMART GUY!

--PERTY GOOD *ARGUING*, HUH?

The Meadow

If sheep desire to show their shepherd how much they have eaten, they do so by digesting the pasture internally, and producing wool and milk externally. They do not vomit up the grass as a demonstration of their good eating.
—Epictetus the Stoic

GOOD ADVICE! BUT I STILL THOUGHT YOU MIGHT LIKE TO SEE SOME OF THE STUFF I'VE BEEN *GRAZING* ON, IN CASE YOU WANT TO *RUMINATE* ON SOME OF IT YOURSELF!

THE BIG PICTURES IN "WATCH JESUS AND THINK TRINITY" ARE COPIED FROM A FIFTEENTH-CENTURY WOODBLOCK BOOK CALLED THE *BIBLIA PAUPERUM* ("THE BIBLE OF THE POOR"). IT'S AN AMAZING BOOK THAT COULD BE YOUR ONE-VOLUME INTRODUCTION TO "HOW TO THINK IN PICTURES" ACCORDING TO THE CHRISTIAN TRADITION. MY FAVORITE MODERN EDITION OF IT IS THE ONE EDITED AND ANNOTATED BY AVRIL HENRY. THE FIVE-CIRCLE FORMAT ON THOSE PAGES IS AN IDEA I GOT FROM A DIFFERENT VERSION OF THE BIBLIA PAUPERUM; IT'S A VERITABLE MEDIEVAL COMIC BOOK! AS FOR THE IDEAS IN THE "WATCH JESUS" SECTION, YOU CAN READ MORE ABOUT THEM IN JÜRGEN MOLTMANN'S *THE TRINITY AND THE KINGDOM; REFLECTED GLORY* AND *THE FORGOTTEN FATHER* BY THOMAS SMAIL; AND *THE PRESENCE AND THE POWER* BY GERALD HAWTHORNE. I THINK I GOT THE PHRASE "THINK TRINITY!" FROM A LECTURE BY STEVE SEAMANDS AT ASBURY THEOLOGICAL SEMINARY.

AS FOR THE PICTURES IN "HOW TO DRAW THE TRINITY," THEY COME FROM ALL OVER THE PLACE, OR AT LEAST ALL OVER MEDIEVAL EUROPE. IF YOU WANT TO READ MORE ABOUT TRINITY IMAGES, START WITH ADOLPHE DIDRON'S *CHRISTIAN ICONOGRAPHY*, OR GEORGE TAVARD'S BOOK *THE VISION OF THE TRINITY*. I WANT TO THANK JANE DILLENBERGER AND DOUG ADAMS FOR TEACHING A GREAT CLASS ON "VISUAL ARTS AS BIBLICAL STUDIES" AT THE GRADUATE THEOLOGICAL UNION IN 1997; THAT'S WHERE I STARTED DOING THIS RESEARCH. I WROTE AND DREW THIS CHAPTER DURING MAY 1997, AND ON THE THIRD OF THAT MONTH I WAS SHOCKED BY THE UNTIMELY DEATH OF CATHERINE MOWRY LACUGNA, A TRINITARIAN THEOLOGIAN WHOSE BOOKS AND ARTICLES HAD TAUGHT ME A LOT. THIS CHAPTER IS DEDICATED TO HER MEMORY.

TRINITY MATH" BRINGS TOGETHER IDEAS FROM THEOLOGIANS LIKE WALTER KASPER AND KALLISTOS WARE, BUT THE BEST PLACE TO START READING WOULD BE BOOK FOUR OF C.S. LEWIS' *MERE CHRISTIANITY*. IF YOU THINK YOU ALREADY KNOW THAT LITTLE BOOK, TRY SKIPPING STRAIGHT TO BOOK FOUR NEXT TIME YOU READ IT; IT'S DYNAMITE! SPECIAL THANKS GO TO BONNIE JOHNSTON FOR SCANNING SOME IMAGES FOR ME ON THIS CHAPTER, AND TO MY WIFE SUSAN FOR PROOFREADING, CRITIQUING AND ENCOURAGING ALL ALONG THE WAY.

—FRED SANDERS